Contents

Tongue-twisters

Limericks

Humorous verse

She sells sea shells

She sells sea shells
    on the sea shore;
The shells she sells are
    sea shells I'm sure.
So if she sells sea shells
    on the sea shore,
I'm sure the shells are
    sea shore shells.

Anonymous

Breakfast for one

Hot thick crusty buttery toast
Buttery toasty thick hot crust
Crusty buttery hot thick toast
Crusty thick hot toasty butter
Thick hot buttery crusty toast
Toasty buttery hot thick crust
Hot buttery thick crusty toast –

With marmalade is how I like it most!

Judith Nicholls

Peter Piper

Peter Piper picked a peck
    of pickled pepper;
A peck of pickled pepper
    Peter Piper picked.
If Peter Piper picked a peck
    of pickled pepper,
Where's the peck of pickled pepper
    Peter Piper picked?

Anonymous

Shop chat

My shop stocks:
  locks, chips,
  chopsticks,
  watch straps,
  traps, tops,
  taps, tricks,
  ship's clocks,
  lipstick and chimney pots.

What does your shop stock?

Sharkskin socks.

Libby Houston

5

How much wood could a woodchuck chuck

How much wood could a woodchuck chuck
If a woodchuck could chuck wood?
As much wood as a woodchuck
would chuck
If a woodchuck could chuck wood.

Anonymous

Tongue-
twister

Betty Botter bought some butter

Betty Botter bought some butter,
But she said "This butter's bitter.
If I put it in my batter,
It will make my batter bitter.
If I bought a bit of butter,
Better than the bitter butter,
It would make my batter better."
So she bought a bit of butter,
Better than the bitter butter,
And it made her batter better.

Anonymous

7

An old man with a beard

There was an old man with a beard,
Who said; "It is just as I feared.
Two owls and a hen,
Five larks and a wren,
Have all built their nests in my beard."

Edward Lear

8

A young farmer of Leeds

There was a young farmer of Leeds,
Who swallowed six packets of seeds.
It soon came to pass
He was covered in grass,
And couldn't sit down for the weeds.

Anonymous

A young man of Bengal

There was a young man of Bengal
Who went to a fancy-dress ball,
He went, just for fun,
Dressed up as a bun,
And a dog ate him up in the hall.

Anonymous

Mister Crumpett

A bridge engineer, Mister Crumpett,
Built a bridge for the good River Bumpett.
A mistake in the plan
Left a gap in the span,
But he said, "Well, they'll just have to jump it."

Anonymous

11

An old poacher called Bruce

There was an old poacher called Bruce
Whose belt was always too loose.
One day in the town
His trousers fell down,
And out came three cats and a goose.

Michael Palin

12

Limerick

A young lady of Twickenham

There was a young lady of Twickenham

Whose boots were too tight to walk quickenham.

She bore them a while

But at last at a stile,

She pulled them both off and was sickenham.

Anonymous

A diner at Crewe

A diner while dining at Crewe
Found quite a large mouse in his stew.
Said the waiter, "Don't shout,
And wave it about,
Or the rest will be wanting one, too!"

Anonymous

14

A dog called Patch

A dog from Sri Lanka called Patch
Sat down on a tree stump to scratch;
But he found that the flea,
Was not one, but three,
And the first of a very large batch.

Michael Palin

Water everywhere

There's water on the ceiling,
And water on the wall.
There's water in the bedroom,
And water in the hall.
There's water on the landing,
And water on the stair.
Whenever Daddy takes a bath,
There's water everywhere.

Valerie Bloom

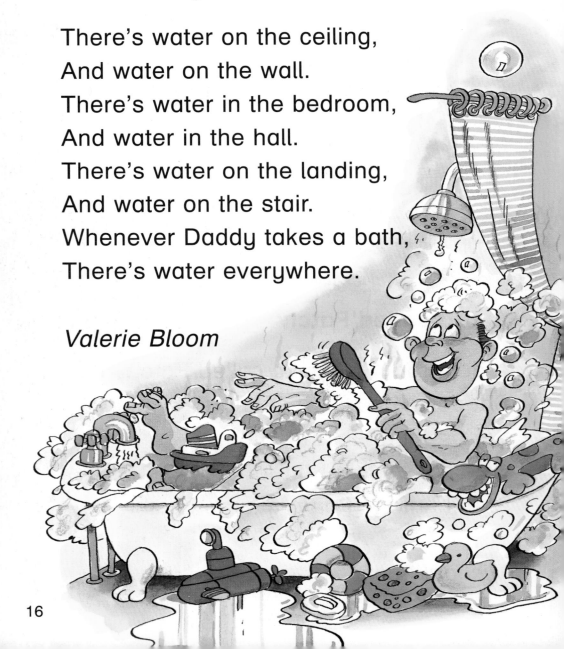

Washing-up day

Clothes in a tub
rub rub rub.
Clothes in a tub
rub rub rub.
Hand in soapy water-o.
Hand in soapy water-o.

Clothes in a tub
rub-um squeeze-um.
Clothes in a tub
rub-um wring-um.
Hand in soapy water-o.
Hand in soapy water-o.

Clothes in a tub
come up nice and clean,
but I saving up
me money
for washing machine.

John Agard

Tummy rumble

My tummy rumbles after breakfast
it rumbles after tea,
it rumbles after dinner
like the roaring rumbling sea.

It rumbles after supper
it rumbles every day,
I wonder why my rumbling tummy
never goes away.

Andrew Collett

Wrong trolley

Mum, there's catfood in our trolley
And we haven't got a cat!
There's a big bag of potatoes
And we didn't load up that.
Do you remember loading beans
Or peas or cauliflowers?
Mum, I know we're pushing it
But is this trolley ours?

Eric Finney

Fisherman's tale

By the canal
I was quietly fishing
when a bowler hat
floated by,
stopped level with my eye
and began to rise.

Below it was a man's head
wearing spectacles;
he asked
"This way to Brackley?"
"Straight ahead."
The face sank back
beneath the wet,
but I was thinking
Brackley's seven miles,
it's getting late;
perhaps he doesn't know
how far

20

I tapped the hat
with my rod; again
the face rose. "Yes?"
"You'll need to hurry
to arrive before dark."
"Don't worry," he said;
"I'm on my bike."

Irene Rawnsley

Rules

Do not jump on ancient uncles.
Do not yell at average mice.
Do not wear a broom to breakfast.
Do not ask a snake's advice.

Do not bathe in chocolate pudding.
Do not talk to bearded bears.
Do not smoke cigars on sofas.
Do not dance on velvet chairs.

Do not take a whale to visit
Russell's mother's cousin's yacht.
And whatever else you do do
It is better you
Do not.

Karla Kuskin

Bubble gum

I'm in trouble
made a bubble
peeled it off my nose

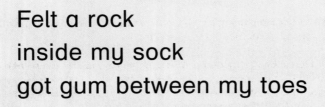

Felt a rock
inside my sock
got gum between my toes

Made another
told my brother
we could blow a pair

Give three cheers
now our ears,
are sticking to our hair.

Nina Payne